THEORY and MUSICIANSHIP by Edith McIntosh

LESSON TWO

THE GREAT STAFF or THE GRAND STAFF

A STAFF is a group of five lines and four spaces.

LINES and SPACES are numbered upwards, from the bottom to the top.

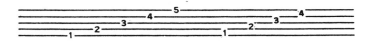

THE GREAT STAFF or GRAND STAFF is made of two staves joined together.

A BRACE and a BAR connect the staves.

TREBLE, the name of the upper staff, means HIGH.

BASS, the name of the lower staff, means LOW.

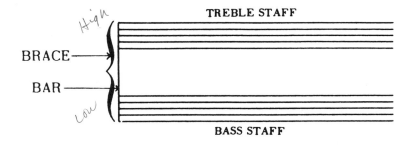

NOTES, placed on the staff, tell us which tones to play or sing.

EACH LINE and EACH SPACE represents one white key on the piano.

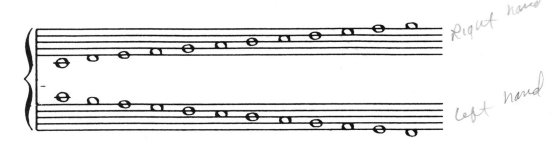

NOTES on the TREBLE STAFF are usually played with the right hand.

NOTES on the BASS STAFF are usually played with the left hand.

THE NOTE on the added line between the staves is MIDDLE C.

CLEFS

A CLEF is a sign placed on the staff to show PITCH.

PITCH is the highness or lowness of tones.

A TREBLE CLEF makes the staff TREBLE. It is also called the G CLEF, because it names the G line.

Practice drawing G CLEFS.

A BASS CLEF makes the staff BASS. It is also called the F CLEF, because it names the F line.

Practice drawing F CLEFS.

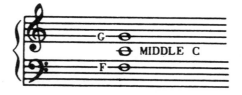

Learn to read all the notes on the staff.

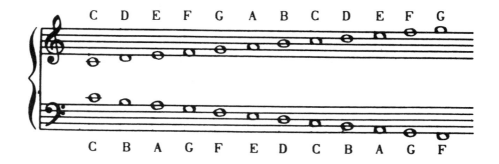

WORK SHEET 2

1. Draw the Brace and the Bar joining these staves to make a Great Staff.

    Print TREBLE on one, BASS on the other.

    Number the lines and the spaces on both Treble and Bass Staves.

    (8)

2. Draw ten G Clefs.

    (10)

3. Draw ten F Clefs.

    (10)

4. The G Clef is also called the _____ Clef.   (1)

5. The F Clef is also called the _____ Clef.   (1)

6. Draw the clefs on this Great Staff.

    Write a whole note (𝅝) on the line named by the G Clef.

    Write a whole note on the line named by the F Clef.

    Write a whole note on Middle C.   (5)

8

7. On the line below the staff print the letter name of each note.

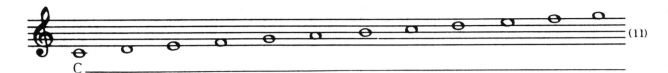

(11)

C _____

8. On this staff write a whole note for each of these letters in two different places.

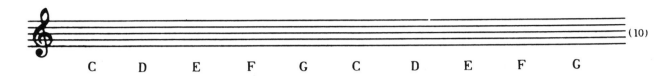

(10)

C   D   E   F   G   C   D   E   F   G

9. On the line below the staff write the letter name of each note.

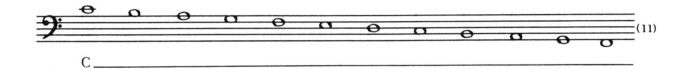

(11)

C _____

10. On this staff write a whole note for each of these letters in two different places.

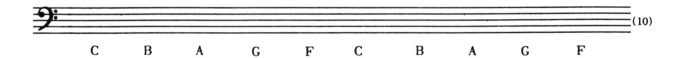

(10)

C   B   A   G   F   C   B   A   G   F

11. Under each of these notes print its name.

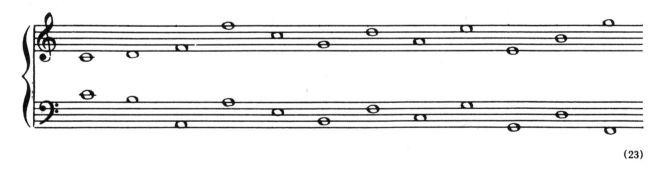

(23)

Pupil's Name _____ Rating _____

Class _____ Teacher _____

Date _____ Marked by _____

THEORY and MUSICIANSHIP by Edith McIntosh

LESSON THREE

OCTAVES and THIRDS on the KEYBOARD

An OCTAVE in our kind of music, is an interval taking in eight consecutive scale degrees. On the keyboard, it is the distance from any key to the next key of the same name, up or down.

Play the white-key octaves A to A, B to B, C to C etc. up and down the keyboard.

Middle C Octave has middle C for its lower note.

THIRDS on the WHITE KEYS. You are playing in thirds when you play every other white key. Each third takes in three white keys. Two you play; the one between, you skip.

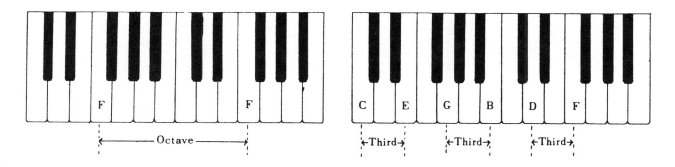

THE MUSIC ALPHABET by THIRDS

THE MUSIC ALPHABET by THIRDS is the MUSIC ALPHABET skipping every other letter.

It should be learned forwards and backwards.

A B̸ C D̸ E F̸ G A̸ B C̸ D E̸ F G̸

A   C   E   G   B   D   F

F   D   B   G   E   C   A

When you say the names of the LINES and SPACES you are saying

the MUSIC ALPHABET by THIRDS.

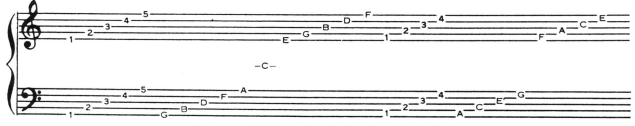

NOTES tell us two things:

    (1) Which keys to play, or which tones to sound.

    (2) How long each tone is to sound.

The length of each tone is measured by beats. Some tones last one beat, some more or less than one beat.

    A quarter note (♩ or ♩) usually gets *one* beat.

    A half note (♩ or ♩) usually gets *two* beats.

    A whole note (○) usually gets *four* beats.

Notice: An "up" stem is placed on the right of the note head.

    A "down" stem is placed on the left of the note head.

1 whole note or 2 half notes or 4 quarter notes will have 4 beats.

$$\text{○} \quad = \quad \text{♩ ♩} \quad = \quad \text{♩ ♩ ♩ ♩} \quad = \quad 4 \text{ beats}$$

A DOT placed after any note adds to the note half the value of the note.

$$\text{♩} \quad + \quad \text{·} \quad = \quad \text{♩ ♩ ♩} \quad = \quad 3 \text{ beats.}$$

$$2 \quad + \quad 1 \quad = \quad 3$$

$$\text{♩} \quad + \quad \text{·} \quad = \quad \text{♩·} \quad = \quad 1\tfrac{1}{2} \text{ beats.}$$

$$1 \quad + \quad \tfrac{1}{2} \quad = \quad 1\tfrac{1}{2}$$

An eighth note (♪ or ♪) gets *half* a beat when the quarter note gets *one* beat.

Notice that the value of the dot is the same as the value of the note next smaller than the note it follows.

Thus:

$$\text{♩·} \quad = \quad \text{♩} \quad + \quad \text{♩}$$

$$\text{♩·} \quad = \quad \text{♩} \quad + \quad \text{♪}$$

WORK SHEET 3

1. Print the Music Alphabet by Thirds, going up.

   Start with A _____ _____ _____ _____ _____ _____ _____

   Start with E _____ _____ _____ _____ _____ _____ _____   (14)

2. Print the Music Alphabet by Thirds, going down.

   Start with G _____ _____ _____ _____ _____ _____ _____

   Start with F _____ _____ _____ _____ _____ _____ _____   (14)

3. Copy on the Great Staff, the notes on the lines and spaces as shown. Print its name under each note.

   (18)

4. Print the names of the lines of the Treble Staff. ____ ____ ____ ____ ____   (5)

5. Print the names of the lines of the Bass Staff. ____ ____ ____ ____ ____   (5)

6. Print the names of the spaces of the Treble Staff. ____ ____ ____ ____   (4)

7. Print the names of the spaces of the Bass Staff. ____ ____ ____ ____   (4)

8. Draw a whole note. _____ (2)

9. Draw two half notes, one with an "up" stem, one with a "down" stem.

   Make the note head first, then add the stem. _____ _____ (4)

10. Draw two quarter notes, one with an "up" stem, one with a "down" stem. _____ _____ (4)

11. Draw two eighth notes, one with an "up" stem, one with a "down" stem. _____ _____ (4)

12. Beside each note write the number of beats it usually has.

    o = _____ beats.   𝅗𝅥 = _____ beats.   ♩ = _____ beat.

    𝅗𝅥. = _____ beats.   ♪ = _____ beat.   (5)

13. Write one note equal to each of the following:

    𝅗𝅥 ♩ ♩ = _____   𝅗𝅥 𝅗𝅥 = _____   𝅗𝅥. 𝅗𝅥 = _____

    ♩ 𝅗𝅥 = _____   ♩ ♩ ♩ = _____   (5)

14. Write these whole notes and name them.

    (1) 1st space treble.   (5) 4th space treble

    (2) 2nd space bass.   (6) 2nd line bass.

    (3) 3rd line treble.   (7) 5th line treble.

    (4) 1st line bass.   (8) 5th line bass.

(12)

Pupil's Name _____ Rating _____

Class _____   Teacher _____

Date _____   Marked by _____

THEORY and MUSICIANSHIP by Edith McIntosh

LESSON FOUR

THE TIME SIGNATURE

To help us count time, the music is divided into boxes or MEASURES, by placing BARS. A DOUBLE BAR is placed at the end of the piece, and elsewhere in the piece to divide it into sections.

The TIME SIGNATURE tells us how to count.

The top number tells us how many beats fill a measure.

The lower number tells the kind of note that gets one beat.

$\frac{2}{4}$ means 2 beats in a measure, a quarter note (♩) gets one beat.

$\frac{3}{4}$ means 3 beats in a measure, a quarter note (♩) gets one beat.

$\frac{4}{4}$ means 4 beats in a measure, a quarter note (♩) gets one beat.

$\frac{3}{8}$ means 3 beats in a measure, an eighth note (♪) gets one beat.

$\frac{4}{8}$ means 4 beats in a measure, an eighth note (♪) gets one beat.

$\frac{6}{8}$ means 6 beats in a measure, an eighth note (♪) gets one beat.

$\frac{4}{2}$ means 4 beats in a measure, a half note (♩) gets one beat.

$\frac{2}{2}$ means 2 beats in a measure, a half note (♩) gets one beat.

Notice that, in drawing an eighth note, the hook is always placed on the right side of the stem. ♪ ♭

Two eighth notes, whether written singly or joined together like this ♫ or ♫ fill the time of a quarter note.

TIME VALUES

Review Lesson Three, Page 10, then study these tables.

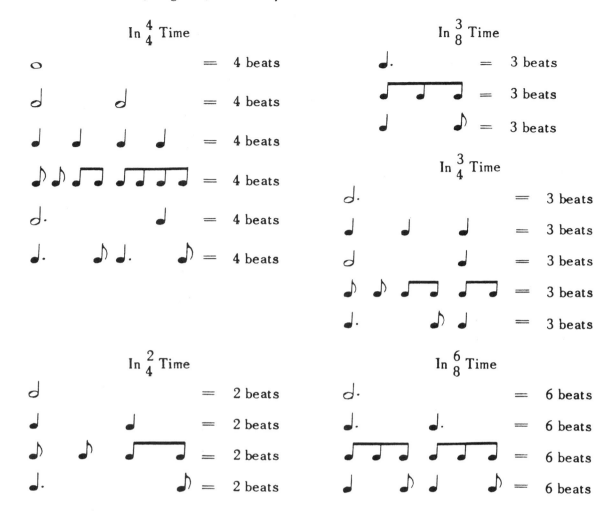

COUNTING

WORK SHEET 4

1. After each of the following TIME SIGNATURES, write the number of beats in the measure, and draw the kind of note that gets one beat.

2/4 ——— beats, a ——— gets one beat.

3/4 ——— beats, a ——— gets one beat.

4/4 ——— beats, a ——— gets one beat.

4/2 ——— beats, a ——— gets one beat.

2/2 ——— beats, a ——— gets one beat.

3/8 ——— beats, an ——— gets one beat.

4/8 ——— beats, an ——— gets one beat.

6/8 ——— beats, an ——— gets one beat.   (16)

2. Draw the bars in this music.

(32)

16

3. Write two different measures of three beats each. Place bars and time signature.

    Use any line or space you choose.

(10)

4. Write two different measures of four beats each. Place bars and time signature.

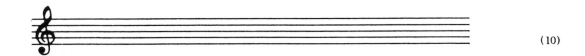

(10)

5. Write the counts in these measures, as in the examples on page 14.

(32)

Pupil's Name _____ Rating _____

Class _____   Teacher _____

Date _____   Marked by _____

N2421

THEORY and MUSICIANSHIP by Edith McIntosh

DRILL SHEET i

1. Print the music alphabet by thirds going up.

    Start with B ___ ___ ___ ___ ___ ___ ___

    Start with D ___ ___ ___ ___ ___ ___ ___   (7)

2. Print the music alphabet by thirds going down.

    Start with C ___ ___ ___ ___ ___ ___ ___

    Start with A ___ ___ ___ ___ ___ ___ ___   (7)

3. Write two measures in each kind of time, all different.

(12)

4. Complete the Grand Staff by drawing a Brace and a Bar. Place the G Clef and the F Clef.

    On the Treble Staff, write a whole note, a half note, a quarter note, and an eighth

    note.

    Write them again on the Bass Staff.

(10)

5. Add notes to complete the following measures. Use as many kinds of notes as you can.

(10)

N 2421

18

6. Write one note that equals the value of each group.

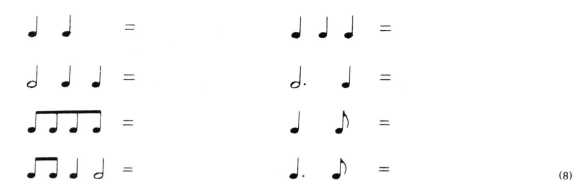

(8)

7. Write whole notes on the Treble Staff and on the Bass Staff.

C G B A F D E

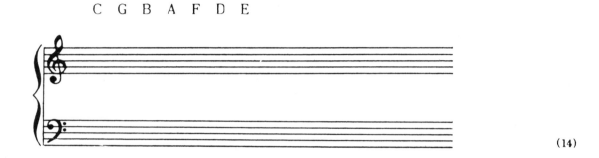

(14)

8. Write the counts for these measures. Write the correct Time Signatures.

(32)

Pupil's Name _____ Rating _____

Class _____ Teacher _____

Date _____ Marked by _____

N 2421

THEORY and MUSICIANSHIP by Edith McIntosh

LESSON FIVE

STAFF STUDY

Each line of the Grand Staff and each space between lines is called a Staff Degree.

The Music Alphabet is used to name the staff degrees.

OCTAVES ON THE STAFF

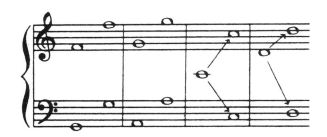

An OCTAVE on the keyboard is the distance from any key to the next key of the same name. An OCTAVE on the staff is the distance from any staff degree to the next staff degree of the same name. The Octave takes in eight staff degrees.

When one note of an octave is on a line, the other is always in a space.

THIRDS ON THE STAFF

A THIRD on the keyboard may be played from one white key to another white key, skipping one white key between. It takes three keys. A THIRD on the staff is the distance between two staff degrees with one staff degree between. The THIRD takes in three staff degrees.

Thirds are written on two lines with one space between, or in two spaces with one line between.

F and G occur in four positions on the Great Staff

The other letter names occur three times on the Great Staff.

HALF STEPS ON THE KEYBOARD.

A HALF STEP on the keyboard is the distance from any key, white or black, to the

very next key.

E to F and B to C are white keys a half step apart.

All other half steps are white-black or black-white.

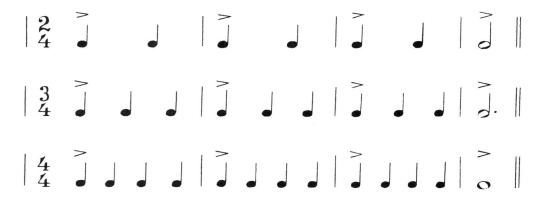

ACCENT is the extra strength or stress with which we play one special beat.

A *measure* accent is the strong beat at the beginning of the measure.

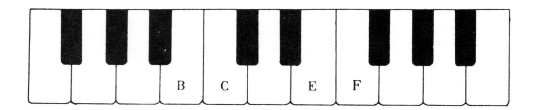

LEGATO, an Italian word, means "bound" or "connected".

Play the music smoothly, each tone exactly joining the next.   OOO

STACCATO, an Italian word, means "detached" or "separated".   O O O

Play the music with short notes, with spaces between them, not joined.

A SLUR is often placed over or under a group of notes as a reminder to play legato.

A DOT (.) is placed over or under a note to indicate staccato.

WORK SHEET 5

1. Use whole notes. In the first measure, write a note that is an octave *above* the given note.

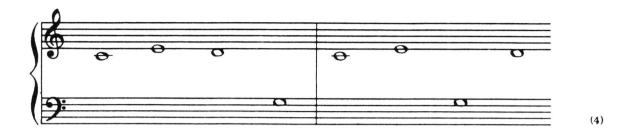

(4)

2. In the second measure above, write a whole note that is an octave *below* each given note.

(4)

3. In whole notes, write a note that is a third *above* each given note.

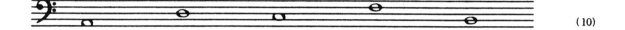

(10)

4. In whole notes write a note that is a third *below* each given note.

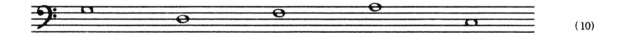

(10)

5. Write, in whole notes on the Grand Staff, all of the F's and G's.

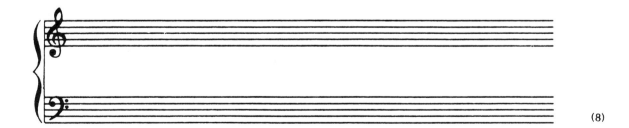

(8)

6. Use whole notes. Write in *three* positions on the Grand Staff G B D F in order.

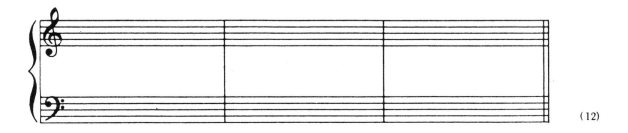

(12)

7. Use whole notes. Write in *three* positions on the Grand Staff F A C E

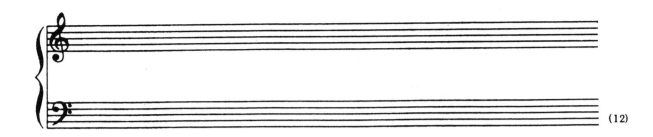

(12)

8. Place stems on these note heads. For notes above the third line, "down" stems.

For notes below the third line, "up" stems. For the third line note, either "up" or "down"

 stem.

9. When tones are smoothly joined, the playing is said to be _____ (4)

10. When tones are short, or there is a break between them, the playing is said to be _____

(4)

11. Mark the first measure in the music to indicate staccato, the second legato.

(8)

12. Notice the Time Signatures. Place Bar Lines. Mark the Measure Accents.

(18)

Pupil's Name _____ Rating _____

Class _____ Teacher _____

Date _____ Marked by _____

THEORY and MUSICIANSHIP by Edith McIntosh

LESSON SIX

SHARPS and FLATS

SHARPS and FLATS on the STAFF.

The sharp (♯) before a note tells us to play the note a half step higher.

The flat (♭) before a note tells us to play the note a half step lower.

The natural (♮) before a note is a reminder to play the white key, not the sharp or flat.

When the ♯ , ♭ or ♮ occurs in the course of the music, it is an ACCIDENTAL.

An ACCIDENTAL affects all the notes on the same line or space, in the same measure only, unless it is canceled by the natural.

The ♯ , ♭ or ♮ is placed *before* the *note* (but *after* the *letter*).

C♯   E♭   B♮

The KEY SIGNATURE is the group of SHARPS or FLATS placed right after the clef.

It means that these sharps or flats are to be used throughout the music.

All the F's, C's, and G's are to be sharped.

All the B's and E's are to be flatted.

N2421

SHARPS and FLATS on the KEYBOARD

EACH BLACK KEY has two names.

Its SHARP name is taken from the white key below it.

Its FLAT name is taken from the white key above it.

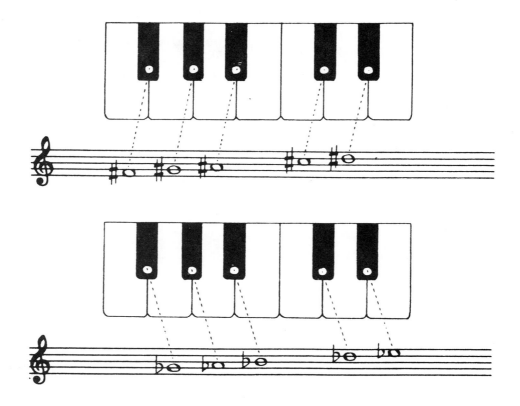

RESTS mean silence. They have different time values like notes.

Notice just how and where they are placed on the staff.

Practice drawing them.

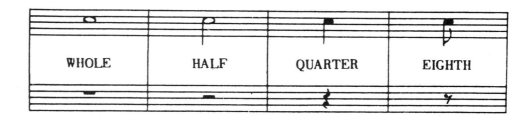

WHOLE	HALF	QUARTER	EIGHTH

Rests, like notes, may be dotted to increase their value by half.

WORK SHEET 6

1. Above each black key print both of its names.

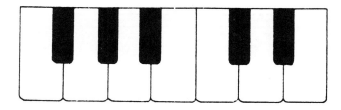

(10)

2. Below each note on the staff print its letter name.

A♭

(18)

3. Write whole notes in three positions above each letter. Be sure to place the sharp or flat to the left of the note, exactly in the space or on the line.

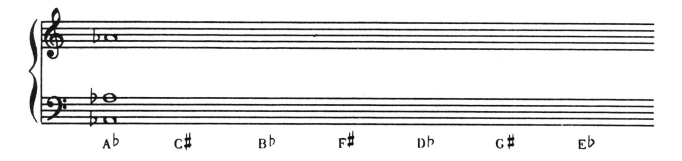

A♭   C♯   B♭   F♯   D♭   G♯   E♭

(18)

4. Draw two rests in each measure, one on the treble staff, one on the bass staff.

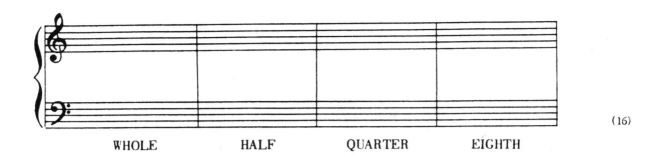

(16)

WHOLE   HALF   QUARTER   EIGHTH

5. Using notes and rests, write four different measures of three beats each.

Place bars and time signature.

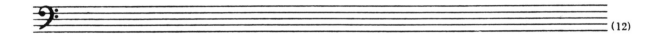

(12)

6. Using notes and rests, write four different measures of four beats each.

Place bars and time signature.

(12)

7. Place bars in this music so that there will be four beats to the measure.

Place the correct time signature at the beginning.

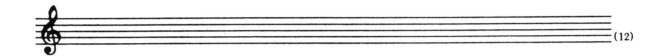

(14)

Pupil's Name _____   Rating _____

Class _____   Teacher _____

Date _____   Marked by _____

THEORY and MUSICIANSHIP by Edith McIntosh

LESSON SEVEN

The SIXTEENTH NOTE and the SIXTEENTH REST

Sixteenth note: ♪ or ♪   Sixteenth rest: ♪

Sixteenth notes and eighth notes may be joined together by cross strokes, and their time values remain the same.

Two sixteenth notes (♬ or ♬) fill the time of an eighth note.

Four sixteenth notes (♬♬ or ♬♬) fill the time of a quarter note.

An eighth and two sixteenth notes (♫ or ♫) also fill the time of a quarter note.

THE TRIPLET

A TRIPLET is a group of three even notes which fills the time of one note.

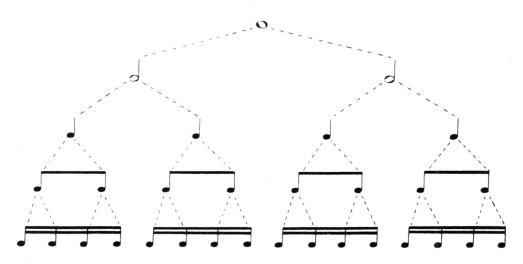

TIME VALUES

NOTES TO BE SOUNDED TOGETHER are printed one above the other.

Played with the same hand on the piano, they are often attached to the same stem.

They are placed on the same side of the stem, except when they are next-door neighbors. Look at the third beat of measure three.

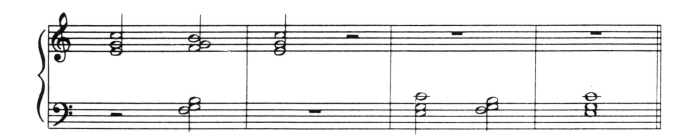

TONES SOUNDED TOGETHER produce HARMONY.

TONES SOUNDED IN SUCCESSION, following each other in an orderly way, make a MELODY.

THE COMBINATION OF LONG and SHORT TONES with ACCENTS is called RHYTHM.

The three elements of music are MELODY, HARMONY, and RHYTHM.

1. Draw two sixteenth notes, one with an "up" stem, one with a "down" stem. _____
(5)

2. Draw one group of four sixteenth notes, joined with a cross stroke, stems "up"_____
(5)

3. Draw one group of four sixteenth notes, joined by a cross stroke, stems "down"_____
(5)

4. Draw a sixteenth rest _____
(5)

5. Write one note equal to each triplet.

(9)

6. Write the triplet which is equal to each single note.

(9)

7. Place stems on these notes.

(14)

8. Write the names of these notes under them. Remember to write the ♯ , ♭ or ♮ to the *right*

   of its letter name.

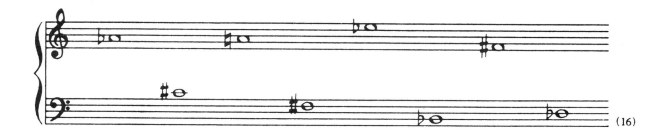

(16)

N2421

9. Complete each measure by adding *one* note.

(8)

10. Complete each measure by adding one rest.

(8)

11. Complete each measure by adding two or four notes.

The whole rest indicates a full measure of silence in any kind of time.

(8)

12. Place the bars and write the counts beneath the notes.

(8)

Pupil's Name _____ Rating _____

Class _____ Teacher _____

Date _____ Marked by _____

THEORY and MUSICIANSHIP by Edith McIntosh

LESSON EIGHT

LEGER LINES

LEGER LINES are ADDED LINES for notes above or below the staff.

Notes ABOVE the Treble Staff.

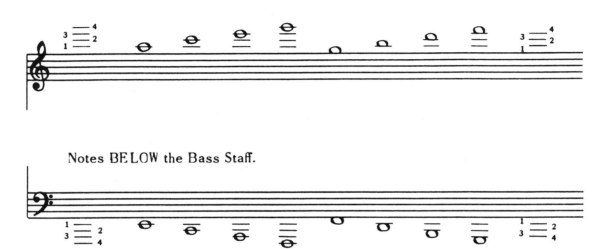

Notes BELOW the Bass Staff.

LEGER LINES and SPACES are named by the MUSIC ALPHABET in THIRDS as are those on the

staff.

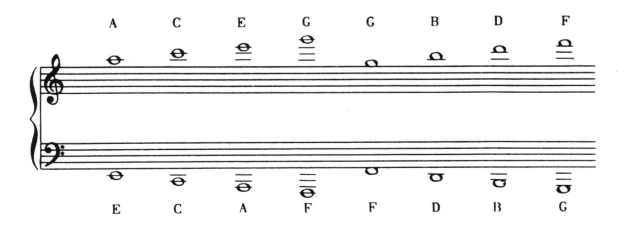

NOTES BETWEEN THE STAVES

Leger Lines are added below the treble staff for Middle C and lower notes.

They are usually played by the right hand.

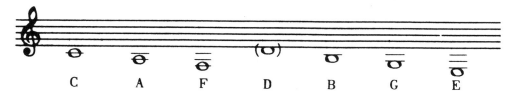

Leger Lines are added above the bass staff for Middle C and higher notes.

They are usually played by the left hand.

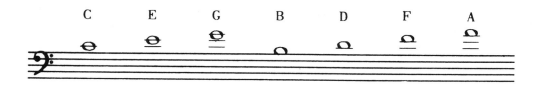

Thus there are two ways of printing the same notes.

THE TIE

THE TIE  is a curved line joining two notes on the same line or space; in other words of

the same pitch. There can be no notes or rests between them. The first note is play-

ed, the second is not played, but its value is added to that of the first note.

The tie joins the note heads, not the stems.

WORK SHEET 8

1. Write the Music Alphabet by thirds going up.

     Start with G. _____

     Start with A. _____   (8)

2. Write the Music Alphabet by thirds, going down.

     Start with F. _____

     Start with E. _____   (8)

3. Print the names of these notes.

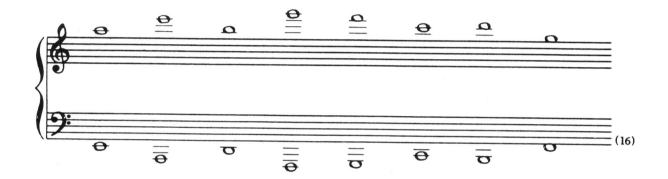

(16)

4. Above each treble note, write one an octave higher.

(12)

5. Below each bass note write one an octave lower.   (12)

6. Write the names of these notes.

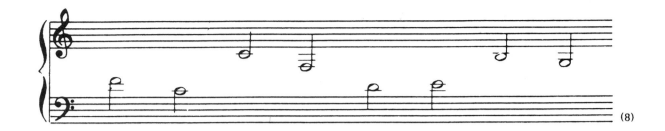

(8)

7. Rewrite these notes, using the treble staff, so that the same piano key would be played.

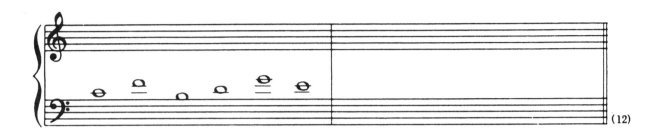

(12)

8. Rewrite these notes, using the bass staff, so that the same piano key would be played.

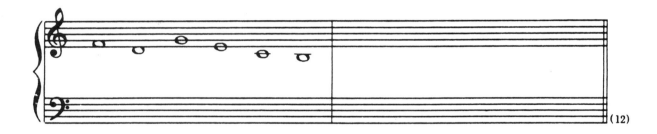

(12)

9. For how many beats will you hold each of these tied notes?

(6)

10. Make an X under each tied note which you play. Cross out the note you do not play.

(6)

Pupil's Name_____ Rating_____

Class_____ Teacher_____

Date_____ Marked by_____

THEORY and MUSICIANSHIP by Edith McIntosh

DRILL SHEET ii

1. Write a note an octave higher, and one an octave lower than each of the notes given. Use whole notes.

(20)

2. Write a note that is a third above each given note. Use whole notes.

(6)

3. Write a note that is a third below each given note. Use whole notes.

(6)

4. Write the letter name of the note that has the sharp, flat, or natural before it.

(10)

5. Put in the bars and mark the measure accents.

(8)

N2421

6. Complete these measures by adding notes and rests.

7. Write whole notes in four positions above each letter. Be sure to place the accidental before

the note, and exactly on the line or in the space.

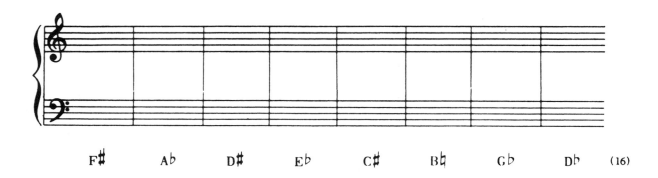

F♯   A♭   D♯   E♭   C♯   B♮   G♭   D♭   (16)

8. Make a treble clef, put in a $\frac{4}{4}$ time signature, then write four measures of notes, using the

following: 𝅗𝅥. | 𝄿 | ♫♫ | 𝄽 | ♪ |

and any other notes and rests you may need to make each measure count right.

(10)

Pupil's Name _____ Rating _____

Class _____ Teacher _____

Date _____ Marked by _____

THEORY and MUSICIANSHIP by Edith McIntosh

LESSON NINE

WHITE KEYS as SHARPS and FLATS

WHITE KEYS must sometimes be used as SHARPS and FLATS.

Study the chart and explain why.

Which keys are so used?

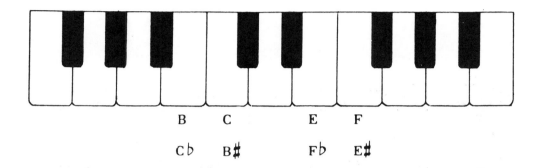

HALF STEPS WRITTEN and SPELLED

Review HALF STEPS ON THE KEYBOARD, LESSON FIVE.

When notes are written differently, yet sound the same, they are called "enharmonic".

There are two ways to "spell" and to write half steps on the staff. Thus:

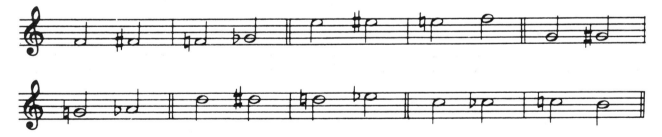

CHROMATIC HALF STEPS are those on the *same* line or space, with the *same* letter name.

DIATONIC HALF STEPS are those on line-space or space-line, next to each other, with *differen*

letter names.

Say the names of the notes above. Which notes sound the same but are "spelled"

differently?

THE MEASURE REST

The WHOLE REST usually means silence for four beats.

It may also mean silence for a WHOLE MEASURE *regardless* of the number of beats.

COMBINATIONS OF NOTES

COMBINATIONS of SHORTER NOTES which fill the value of longer notes.

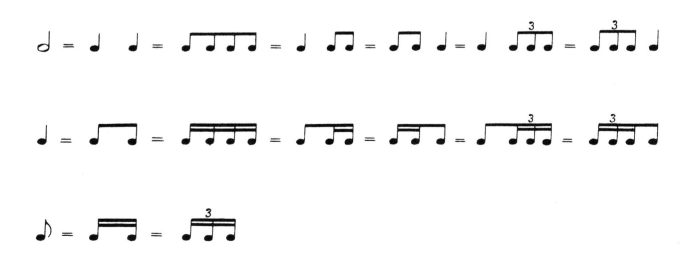

WORK SHEET 9

1. Write two names for each white key marked with a X.

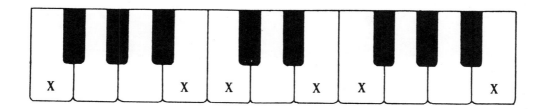

(6)

2. Show two ways to write a half step above G and a half step above B.

(12)

3. Show two ways to write a half step below C and a half step below F.

(12)

4. Mark each Diatonic Half Step (D)   (8)
   and each Chromatic Half Step (C).

5. Write one note which equals each group of notes.

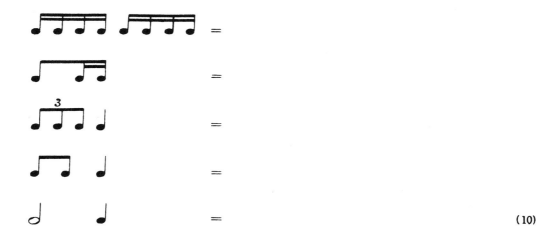

(10)

6. In this music there are missing beats.

   Add just one note in each measure to complete it. Every measure must have four beats.

 (12)

7. Add a group of two or more notes in each measure to complete it.

 (12)

8. Add rests in the places indicated to complete these measures.

 (18)

9. Fill in the number of beats for each group of notes, if in 4/4 time.

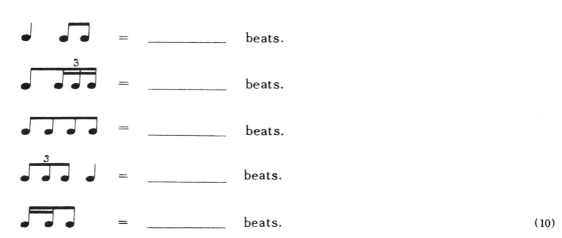

= _____ beats.

= _____ beats.

= _____ beats.

= _____ beats.

= _____ beats.   (10)

Pupil's Name _____ Rating _____

Class _____   Teacher _____

Date _____   Marked by _____

THEORY and MUSICIANSHIP by Edith McIntosh

LESSON TEN

WHOLE STEPS

WHOLE STEPS ON THE KEYBOARD

A whole step is made up of two half steps.

Two white keys, if there is a black key between.

Two black keys, if there is a white key between.

Otherwise, white-black or black-white, with a white key between.

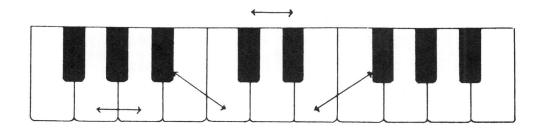

WHOLE STEPS ON THE STAFF

Whole steps are written on staff degrees next to each other, line-space or space-line.

They are spelled with two letter names, next to each other in the alphabet.

Whole steps higher:

Whole steps lower:

MUSICAL TERMS

ITALIAN has come to be the "language of music" for various reasons, among them the following:

Long ago, the best musicians either lived in Italy or went there to study.

Guido, the first musician to use staves and clefs for writing music, was Italian.

The first printed music came from Italy.

The first piano was made in Italy.

The first opera was written in Italy.

f   (*forte*) means loud.

p   (*piano*) means soft.

mf   (*mezzo forte*) means medium loud.

mp   (*mezzo piano*) means medium soft.

cresc.   (*crescendo*) means gradually louder.

——————————— is the sign used to indicate crescendo.

dim.   (*diminuendo*) means gradually softer.

decresc.   (*decrescendo*) also means gradually softer.

——————————— is a sign used to indicate diminuendo and decrescendo.

——————————— Both signs are used together to indicate a swell, the music growing

gradually louder, then softer.

rit.   (*ritardando*) means gradually slower.

rall.   (*rallentando*) also means gradually slower.

riten.   (*ritenuto*) means immediately slower.

WORK SHEET 10

1. Write on the staff a whole note which is a whole step *higher* than the given note.

(14)

2. Write on the staff a whole note which is a whole step *lower* than the given note.

(14)

3. Write the name of a note which is a whole step *higher* than each of the following:

A _____	B _____	B♭ _____
C _____	D _____	E♭ _____
E _____	F _____	D♯ _____
G _____	C♯ _____	A♭ _____ (24)

4. Write the name of a note which is a whole step *lower* than each of the following:

F _____	E _____	E♭ _____
D♯ _____	C _____	B♭ _____
B _____	A _____	D♭ _____
G _____	A♭ _____	F♯ _____ (24)

5. Tell the meaning of each of the following musical terms:

f _____

p _____

mf _____

mp _____

rit. _____ (10)

6. Draw the sign for crescendo.

What does it mean? _____ (7)

7. Draw the sign for diminuendo.

What does it mean? _____ (7)

Pupil's Name_____ Rating_____

Class_____ Teacher_____

Date_____ Marked by_____

THEORY and MUSICIANSHIP by Edith McIntosh

LESSON ELEVEN

DOTTED NOTES and RESTS

A DOT after a note or rest adds to the note or rest half its value.

DOTTED NOTE FIGURES

A MUSICAL FIGURE is a short group of notes making a little pattern. It may be melodic or rhythmic or both.

These dotted-note figures or dotted-note groups are often seen in music.

DOUBLE SHARPS — DOUBLE FLATS

DOUBLE SHARP sign: ✖ A note with this sign before it is played 2 half steps higher.

      C ✖ is played D

      F ✖ is played G

      G ✖ is played A

DOUBLE FLAT sign: ♭♭ A note with this sign before it is played 2 half steps lower.

      D♭♭ is played C

      B♭♭ is played A

      G♭♭ is played F

MORE MUSICAL TERMS AND SIGNS

The FERMATA (⌢) sometimes called a pause or hold, means to hold the note or rest longer than its normal value.

Used over a double bar, it means "pause" before going on.

𝄋 A repetition sign.

D. S. (*Dal Segno*) means "go back to the sign" 𝄋 and repeat to the end.

Fine means the end.

D. C. (*Da Capo*) means "go back to the head or beginning".

REPEAT SIGNS

Play twice, the music from the beginning to the first pair of dots.

Play twice, the music between the two pairs of dots.

TWO ENDINGS

Play the music through the first ending ⌐1⌐ and go back to the beginning.

Then repeat the first two measures and skip to the second ending ⌐2⌐

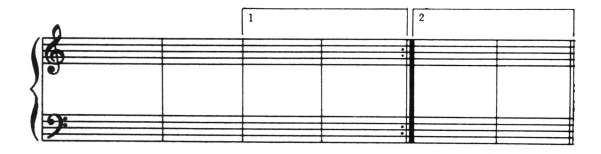

N2421

WORK SHEET 11

1. Write the number of beats for each group of notes, when the quarter note has one beat.

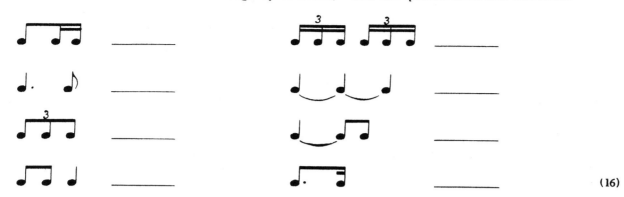

    (16)

2. Write one note that equals each group.

    (18)

3. Fill the blank space with *one* note.

    (12)

4. Fill each blank space with *one* rest.

    (12)

48

5. Write the abbreviation which stands for each of the following musical terms:

Tell what it means.

forte _____ _____

piano _____ _____

mezzo piano _____ _____

mezzo forte _____ _____

crescendo _____ _____

diminuendo _____ _____ (18)

6. Write the following notes on the staff, placing the correct sign before each note.

C double sharp   B double flat   G sharp   D natural   (8)

7. Write the name below each of the following notes.

(8)

8. Write the name of the piano key we use to play the following notes.

C✖   G✖   D♭♭   B♭♭   (8)

Pupil's Name _____ Rating _____

Class _____ Teacher _____

Date _____ Marked by _____

N 2421

THEORY and MUSICIANSHIP by Edith McIntosh

LESSON TWELVE

INTERVALS

An INTERVAL is the difference in pitch between two sounds, or tones.

INTERVALS have number names reckoned from the number of letter names used in forming them.

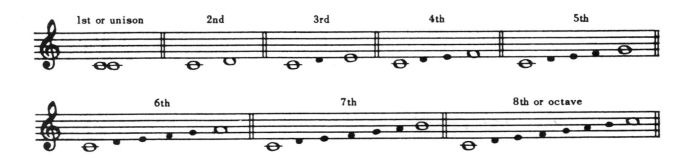

The tones of an interval may be sounded separately as a melody, or together as a chord.

The change of one or both notes of an interval by an accidental does not change its number name. Thus each of the following is a third, as there is only one letter name, D, between them.

Study and name these intervals.

THE MUSIC ALPHABET BY FIFTHS

When we say the MUSIC ALPHABET BY THIRDS we skip every other letter in the MUSIC ALPHABET.

When we say the MUSIC ALPHABET BY FIFTHS, we skip every other letter in the MUSIC ALPHABET BY THIRDS.

```
A B C D E F G A B C D E F G A B C D E F G A B C D E F G A
A   C   E   G   B   D   F   A   C   E   G   B   D   F   A
A       E       B       F       C       G       D       A
```

Practice saying the MUSIC ALPHABET BY FIFTHS forwards and backwards.

FIFTHS are written on the staff line-line, with one line between, or space-space with one space between.

OTHER INTERVALS ON THE STAFF

THIRDS, FIFTHS, and SEVENTHS (3rds, 5ths, 7ths) are written line-line or space-space.

SECONDS, FOURTHS, SIXTHS and OCTAVES (2nds, 4ths, 6ths, 8ths) are written line-space or space-line.

REVIEW OF WHOLE TONES and SEMITONES

WHOLE TONE is another name for WHOLE STEP. SEMITONE is another name for HALF STEP.

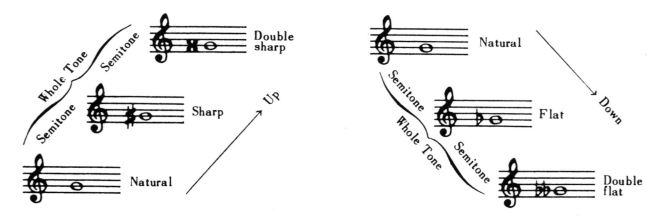

WORK SHEET 12

1. Write the Music Alphabet by Thirds going up. Start with C.

  ____ ____ ____ ____ ____ ____ ____ ____ (4)

2. Write the Music Alphabet by Fifths going up. Start with G.

  ____ ____ ____ ____ ____ ____ ____ (4)

3. Write the number names of intervals written line-line or space-space.

  ____ ____ ____ (3)

4. Write the number names of intervals written line-space or space-line.

  ____ ____ ____ ____ (4)

5. Write the interval of a 2nd beside each of the following notes.

(12)

6. Write the interval of a 3rd above each of the first three notes, a 3rd below each of the others.

(12)

7. Write, beside each given note, a note which is a 5th above it.

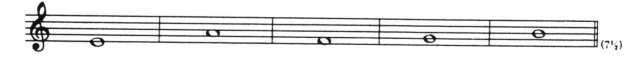

(7½)

8. Write, beside each given note, a note which is a 6th below it.

(7½)

9. Write octaves above the following notes.

(10)

10. Write octaves below the following notes.

(12)

11. Write the number name under each of the following intervals.

(12)

12. Write a note which is a whole tone above the given note.
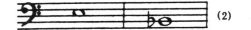
(2)

13. Write a note which is a whole tone below the given note.
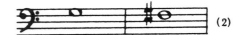
(2)

14. Write a note which is a semitone above the given note, then one which is a semitone below it.

(8)

Pupil's Name_____ Rating_____

Class_____ Teacher_____

Date_____ Marked by _____

THEORY and MUSICIANSHIP by Edith McIntosh

DRILL SHEET iii

1. Fill each blank space with a triplet.

(6)

2. Write as many quarter notes as are needed to equal each of the following:

(24)

3. Write as many eighth notes as are needed to equal each of the following:

(18)

4. Write as many sixteenth notes as would equal each of the following. Join them with cross strokes.

(15)

54

5. Draw the note equal in value to each rest.

▅ = _____   𝄾 = _____

▅ = _____

𝄽 = _____

𝄾 = _____   (5)

6. Rewrite using dotted notes instead of tied notes.

♩♩♩ _____   ♫♫ _____   ♩♪ _____

♩♫ _____   ♩♩ _____   ♪♪ _____   (18)

7. Fill each blank space with two notes of equal value.

♩ + _____ = o   ♩. ♪ + _____ = ♩.

♩ + _____ = ♩

♪ + _____ = ♩   (8)

8. Fill each blank space with two notes, one of them dotted.

♩ + _____ = o

♩ + _____ = ♩   (6)

Pupil's Name _____ Rating _____

Class _____   Teacher _____

Date _____   Marked by _____

THEORY and MUSICIANSHIP by Edith McIntosh

EXAMINATION

1. Write the Music Alphabet by Thirds going down. Begin and end with F. (6)

2. Write the Music Alphabet by Fifths going up. Begin and end with D. (6)

3. Print the names under these notes.

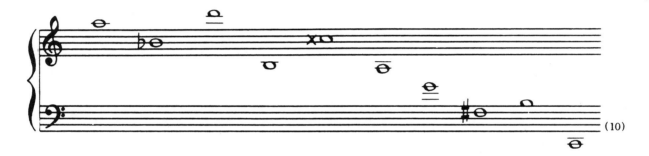

(10)

4. Draw a Brace and a Bar to connect the staves.

   Draw a perfect G clef and an F clef.

   In the Treble, write a Whole note, Half note, Quarter note, Eighth note, Sixteenth note.

   In the Bass, write a rest of the same value under each note.

Whole	Half	Quarter	Eighth	Sixteenth

(12)

5. Complete these measures. Use notes and rests.

(6)

6. Using the given note, write a note which is:

      (1) A whole step higher.

      (2) A whole step lower.

      (3) A Diatonic half step higher.

      (4) A Chromatic half step lower.

      (5) A 3rd above.

      (6) A 5th below.

      (7) A 6th above.

      (8) A 7th below.

      (9) An octave higher.

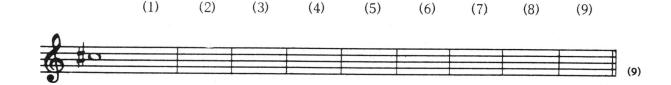

(9)

7. Write one note equal to each of the following:

(6)

8. Write another letter name for:

C _____   F _____   B _____   E _____   G _____

(5)

9. Place the bars in their proper places.

(10)

10. Print "W" under each whole step, "H" under each half step.

(6)

11. Mark these measures to show:

    (a) The first staccato.

    (b) The second legato.

    (c) All to be repeated.

(3)

12. Write abbreviations or signs for terms meaning:

loud _____ soft _____ medium loud _____ gradually louder _____

gradually softer _____ gradually slower _____ flat _____

pause _____ "go back to the beginning" _____ sharp _____ double sharp _____ (11)

13. Under each interval write its number name.

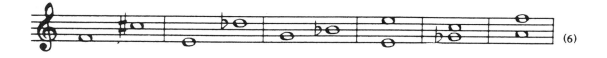

(6)

14. Write four measures, $\frac{4}{4}$ time, all different, using 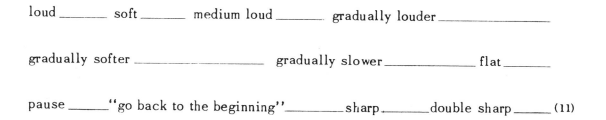 and any other notes and rests.

(4)

58

Pupil's Name_____ Rating_____

Class_____ Teacher_____

Date_____ Marked by_____

N2421

THEORY
and
MUSICIANSHIP

Book 1

Lessons in
the Rudiments of Music
with Work Sheets

For Beginners of all Ages

EDITH McINTOSH

BLESSING MUSIC COMPANY

210 E. Jackson Blvd.
Elkhart, Indiana 46516
(219) 293-6332

CARL FISCHER®
65 Bleecker Street, New York, NY 10012

O3926

ISBN 0-8258-0261-X